Bud the Pup

by Peyton Walston
illustrated by Hector Borlasca

Target Skill Short *Uu*/u/
High-Frequency Words *what, said, was*

Jem was sad.

"Look in the box, Jem," said Mom.

"See what is in the box."

It is Bud the pup.

"Come and see Bud the pup,"
said Jem.
"He is little and fun!"

Jan and Rex like little Bud.

Jem likes Bud.

The pup is fun.

Look what Bud can do!

Bud likes to tug.

He likes to tug on the rug.

Bud can run and jump.

Bud can have fun in the sun.

Jem, Rex, and Jan have fun in the sun.

It was fun.

We had fun with Bud.

Jem likes Bud.